Dear Parent,

Sharing a book is the perfect opp
with your child. Research has show
your child is probably the single mc
prepare him or her for success in sc ....ook
with your child, not only are you help ......ginen his or her
reading and vocabulary skills, you are also stimulating your child's
curiosity, imagination and enthusiasm for reading.

Join Mater and his cousins as they create great music in the scrapyard
and discover hidden talents none of them knew they had! Ask your
child to tell you his or her favourite way to express him or herself. Is it
by painting or singing? Dancing or telling jokes? Being able to connect
to a story, by thinking about personal experiences that are similar,
is an important strategy that enables readers to more fully understand
and engage with the story.

Children learn in different ways and at different speeds. Remember,
successful readers have one thing in common: supportive, loving adults
who share books with them often, to nurture a lifelong love of books,
reading and learning.

Enjoy your reading adventure together!

First published by Parragon in 2012
Parragon
Chartist House
15–17 Trim Street
Bath BA1 1HA, UK
www.parragon.com

Consultants: Cheryl Stroud, English Language Arts Curriculum Leader and Reading Specialist,
Concord Road Elementary School, Ardsley, NY; Beth Sycamore, Literacy Consultant, Chicago, IL

Editor: Joëlle Murphy

Designer: Scott Petrower

Illustrated by the Disney Storybook Artists

ISBN 978-1-78186-027-4

Printed in China

Let's Play

Parragon

Bath • New York • Singapore • Hong Kong • Cologne • Delhi
Melbourne • Amsterdam • Johannesburg • Shenzhen

Mater has many cousins.
He has a cousin named Jud.

He has a cousin named Cletus.

He has a cousin named Buford.

Mater loves to play with his cousins.
They like to meet at the scrapyard.

Bubba sees Mater and his cousins.

Bubba is big and mean.

He doesn't like to play anything!

"Look-ee here!" shouts Jud.

Jud rolls a tyre.

"I love playing with tyres," he says.

"That looks fun!" says Mater.

Bubba pushes Mater.

He kicks the tyre.

"I don't like tyres," says Bubba.

Bubba is not good at rolling tyres.

9

"Look-ee here!" shouts Cletus.

Cletus spins a bumper.

"I love playing with bumpers," he says

"That looks fun!" says Mater.

Bubba pushes Mater.

He kicks the bumper.

"I don't like bumpers," says Bubba.

Bubba is not good at spinning bumpers.

"Look-ee here!" shouts Buford.

Buford throws a hubcap.

"I love playing with hubcaps," he say

"That looks fun!" says Mater.

ubba pushes Mater.

e kicks the hubcap.

don't like hubcaps," says Bubba.

ubba is not good at throwing hubcaps.

Mater looks at Bubba.

Jud looks at Bubba.

Cletus and Buford look at Bubba.

"Go away!" they shout.

Bubba spins his tyres.

He slams his hook.

Then he honks his horn.

HONK! HONK-A-HONK! HONK!

Mater smiles at Bubba.
"Bubba, you are good at honking
your horn!" Mater shouts.

I am?" Bubba asks.

Let's play!" he says.

Jud loves tyres, so he plays one.
PLINK, PLINK-A-PLINK, PLINK!

That's cool," says Cletus.

Cletus loves bumpers, so he plays or
WHAP, WHAP-A-WHAP, WHAP!

'That's cool," says Buford.

Buford loves hubcaps, so he plays on
PLING, PLING-A-PLING, PLING!

"That's cool," says Bubba.

Bubba loves his horn, so he plays it.
HONK! HONK-A-HONK! HONK!

"That's cool," says Mater.

Mater loves music, so he dances!

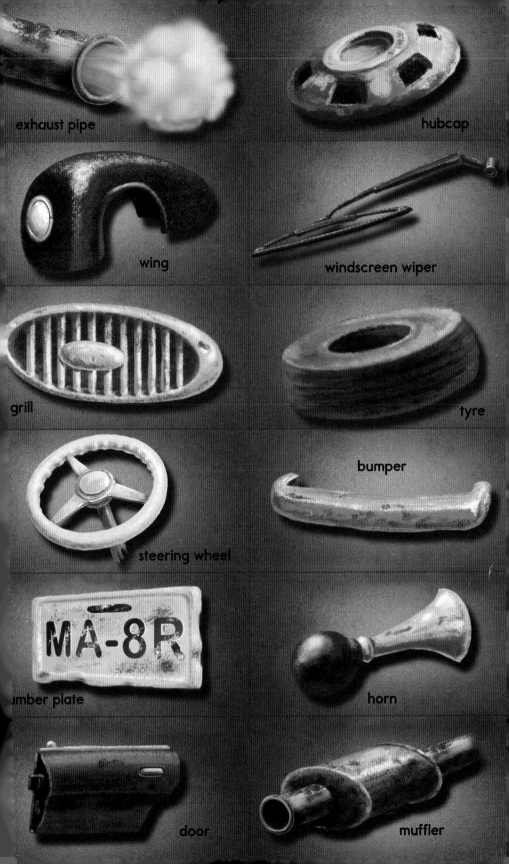

exhaust pipe

hubcap

wing

windscreen wiper

grill

tyre

bumper

steering wheel

umber plate

horn

door

muffler

Join the Band!

Join the Band!

Join the Band!

Join the Band!

Join the Band!

Join the Band!

Join the Band!

Join the Band!

Join the Band!

Join the Band!

Join the Band!

Join the Band!

Join the Band!

A game for 2-3 players

ter and his cousins made instruments from things that they love.
y want you to join their band! What can you bring to play?

up

a grown-up to cut out the cards on page 27, following the dotted pink
s. Mix up the cards and place them face down in a pile.

y Join the Band!

first player says, "I am in the band and I'm going to play...." He or
then takes the top card from the pile of cards and looks at it, naming
picture that is on the card and making a sound that the instrument
ht make. That player then places the card face down in front of them.

second player repeats the phrase and repeats what the first
trument" was and the sound it made. The second player then takes
top card from the pile of cards and names the instrument that he or
will play. That player then places the card face down in front of them.

example:

ayer 1 draws a **windscreen wiper** card: "I am in the band and I'm going
play a windscreen wiper! *Whup-a-whup, whup-a-whup, whup-a-whup.*"

ayer 2 draws a **grill** card: "I am in the band and I'm going to play a
ndscreen wiper! *Whup-a-whup, whup-a-whup, whup-a-whup* – and a
ill – *zzzz-zz-zzz, zzzz-zz-zzz, zzzz-zz-zzz!*"

ayer 3 draws an **exhaust pipe** card: "I am in the band and I'm going
play a windscreen wiper – *whup-a-whup, whup-a-whup, whup-a-whup*
and a grill – *zzzz-zz-zzz, zzzz-zz-zzz, zzzz-zz-zzz* – and an exhaust
pe – *clangety-clang, clangety-clang, clangety-clang!*"

game continues until all of the cards
been played, or someone forgets
order of instruments or the sound
instrument makes. Then the fun
start all over again!

Mini book sticker fun!

In *Let's Play*, Bubba starts a band and learns to get along with Mater and Mater's cousins. Now you can make a 'mini book' to retell the story.

Ask a grown-up to cut out the 'mini book', following the pink dotted lines. Lay pages 4 and 5 on top of pages 2 and 7. Fold the book in half along the blue lines and staple the pages together.

Now you can match each character sticker on your sticker sheet to the correct page. When you are finished, find someone you can read your book to.

Bubba's Band

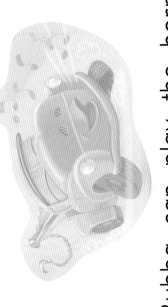

Bubba can play the horn.

Jud can play the tyre.

And Mater
can dance!

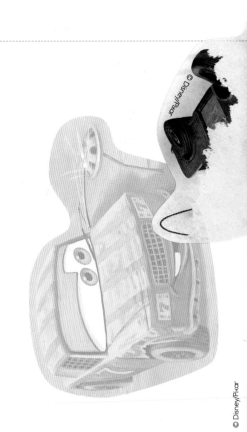

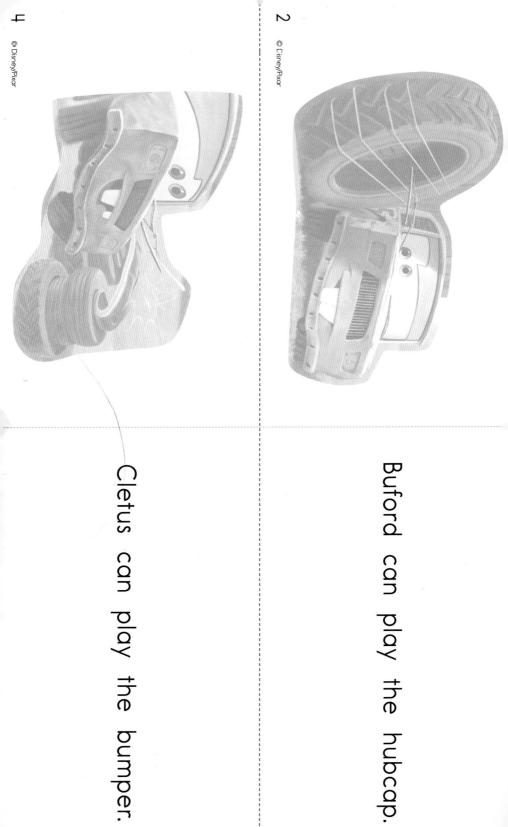

Buford can play the hubcap.

Cletus can play the bumper.